Footprints at Birth

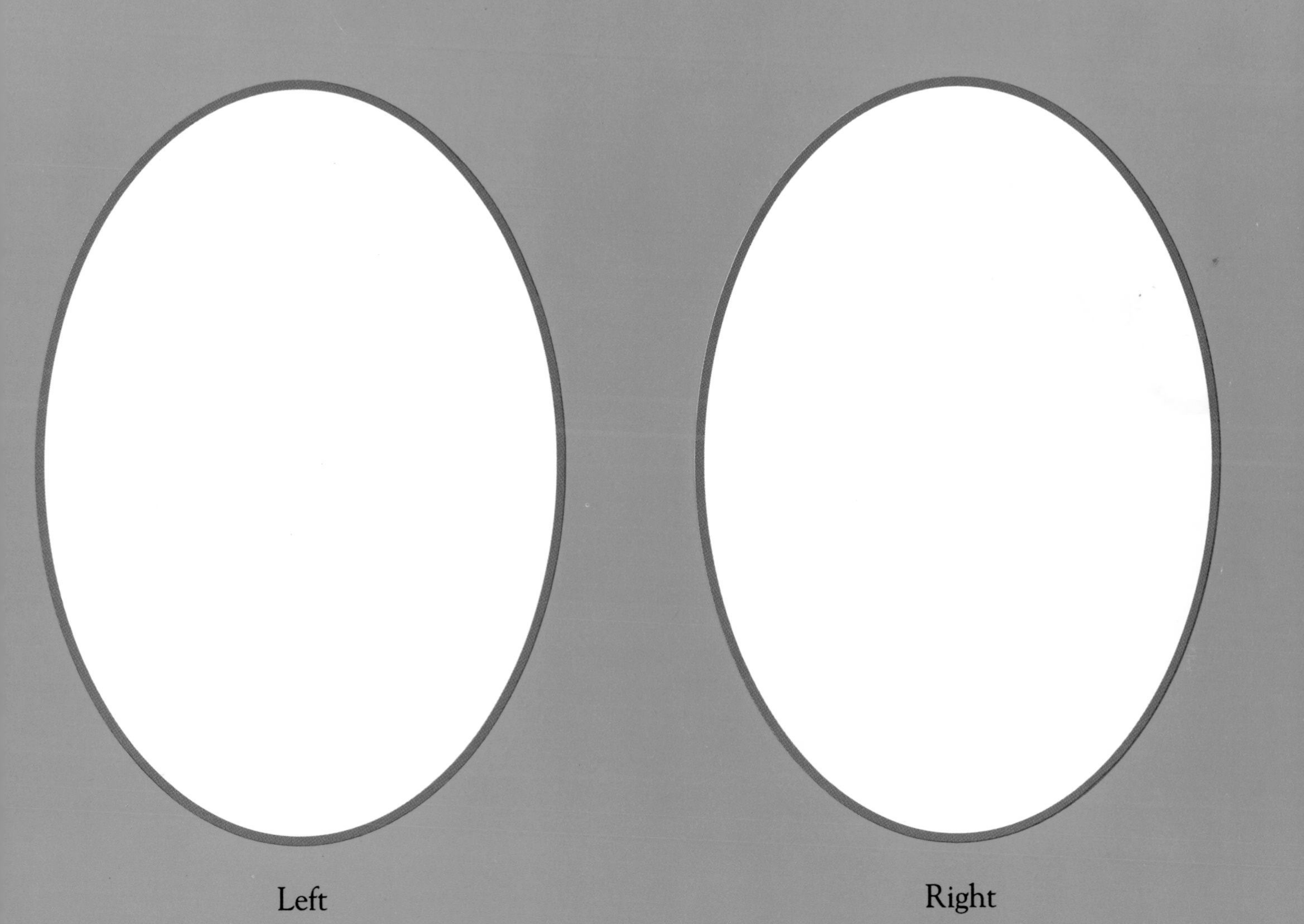

CARL'S BABY JOURNAL

ALEXANDRA DAY

Farrar Straus Giroux
New York

Names Considered

BOYS' NAMES

GIRLS' NAMES

This is the Baby Book of

BABY'S FIRST PHOTOGRAPH

born on

at o'clock

at (place)

hair color

eye color

length

weight

Date

The

Baby's name

Father
Birthplace
Date

Grandfather
Birthplace
Date

Grandmother
Birthplace
Date

Great-grandfather
Birthplace
Date

Great-grandfather
Birthplace
Date

Great-grandmother
Birthplace
Date

Great-grandmother
Birthplace
Date

Family

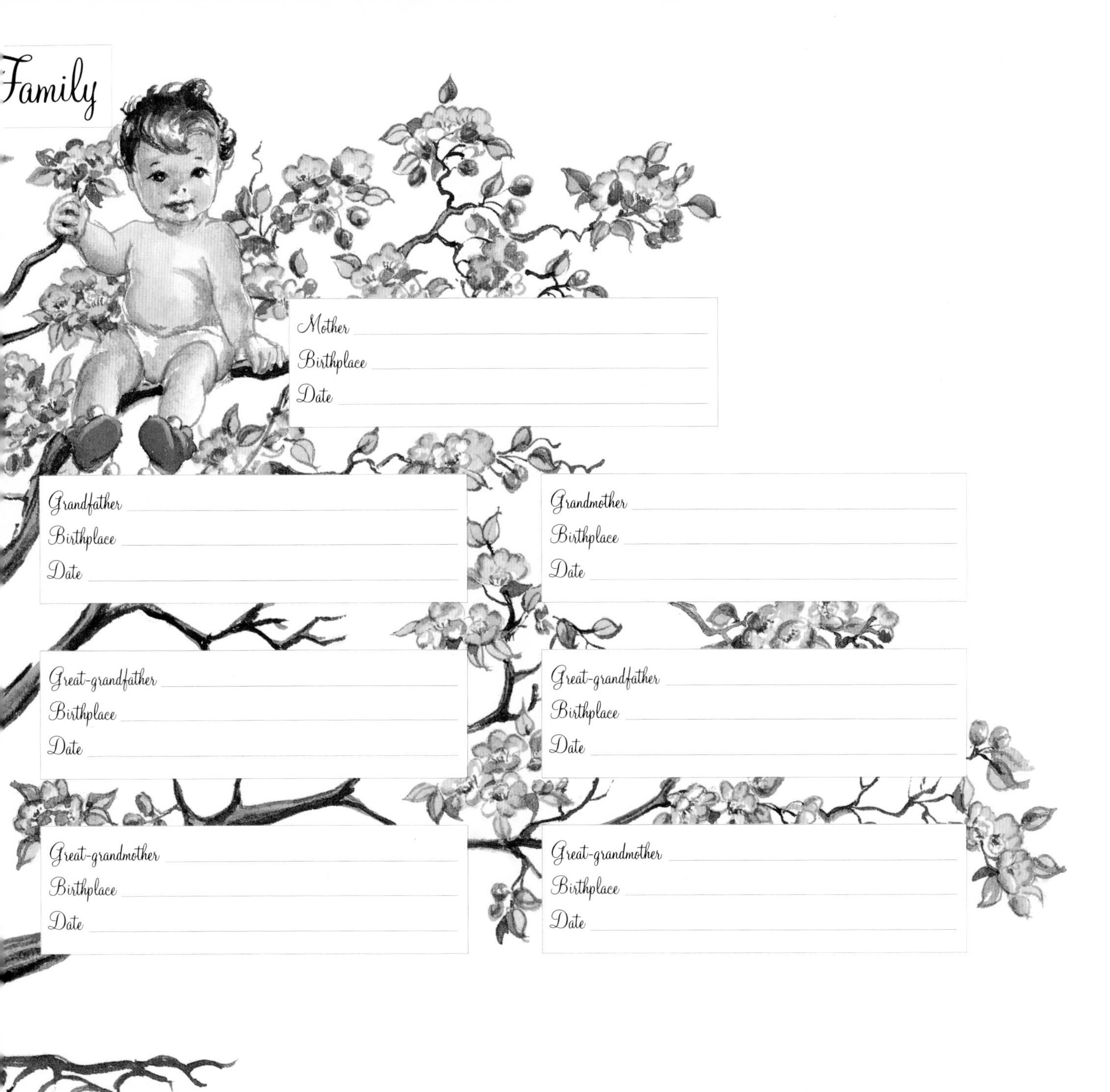

Mother
Birthplace
Date

Grandfather
Birthplace
Date

Grandmother
Birthplace
Date

Great-grandfather
Birthplace
Date

Great-grandfather
Birthplace
Date

Great-grandmother
Birthplace
Date

Great-grandmother
Birthplace
Date

Religious Observance

Place of Observance ______________________ Date __________

Officiant ______________________________

Signature of Officiant ______________________________

Witnesses, godparents, or other participants ______________________________

____

Birth Certificate

Family Portraits

PHOTOGRAPH

Name(s) ____________________

Date ____________________

PHOTOGRAPH

Name(s) ____________________

Date ____________________

PHOTOGRAPH

Name(s) ____________________

Date ____________________

Family Portraits

PHOTOGRAPH

Name(s) ____________________

Date ____________________

Visitors...

And What They Said

Gifts

Thank-you note sent

Gifts

Thank-you note sent

Friends Who Helped and Things They Lent for Baby

Baby's Bath

Date ______________________________

Age of first bath ______________________

Smiles and Laughter

PHOTOGRAPH

Date ______________________

Age of first smile ______________________

PHOTOGRAPH

Date ______________________

Age of first laugh ______________________

First Outing

PHOTOGRAPH

Date ______________________

Destination ______________________

Baby Sits Up

PHOTOGRAPH

Baby's first bottle was on ______________

It contained ______________

____

Date ______________

Age baby first sat up ______________

First Tooth

PHOTOGRAPH

Date ____________________

Age baby cut first tooth ____________________

Age baby first used a spoon ____________________

Baby Crawls

PHOTOGRAPH

Date ______________________

Age baby started to crawl ____________

Baby Stands

PHOTOGRAPH

Date

Age baby first stood

Walking—Running—Skipping—Jumping

PHOTOGRAPH

Date ______________________

Age baby first walked ______________________

PHOTOGRAPH

Date ______________________

Lock of Baby's Hair

Baby's first haircut was on ______________

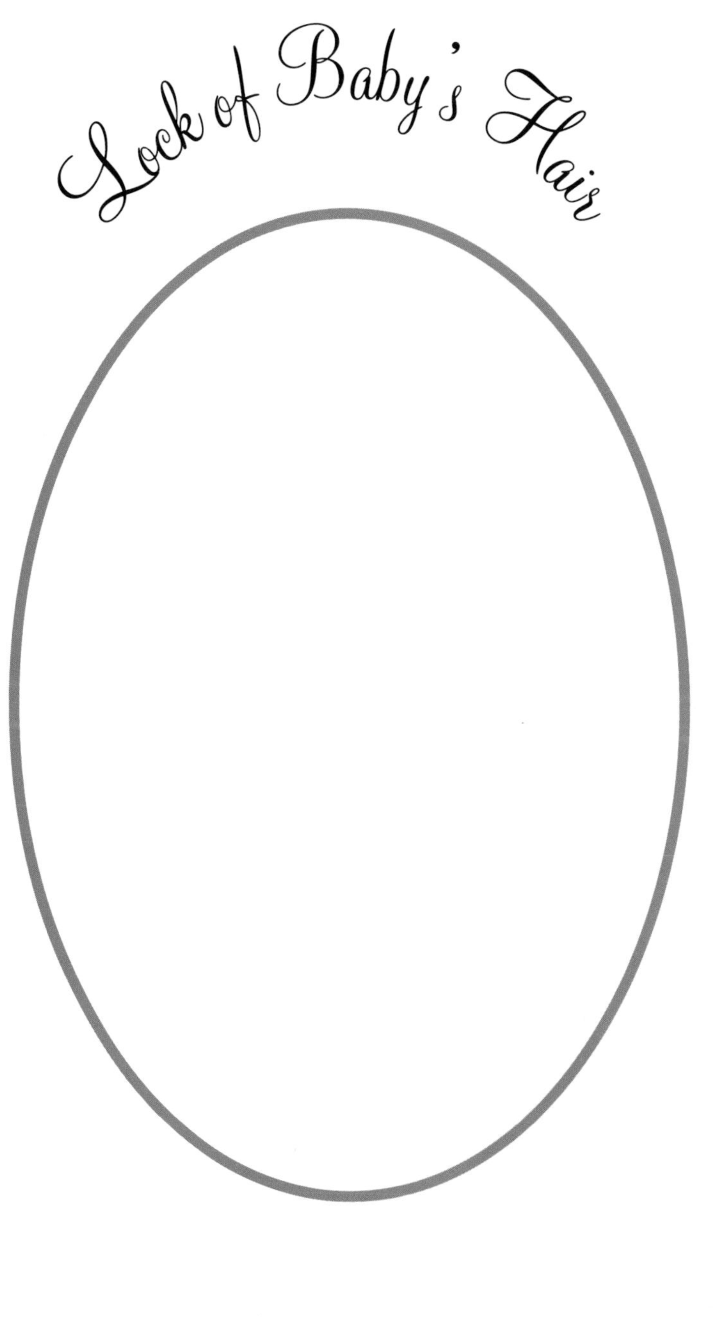

First Words

Age

First Shoes

Age when first worn

Memorable Actions and Sayings

Favorite Toys

Favorite Songs

PHOTOGRAPH

Name(s) ______________________

Date ______________________

PHOTOGRAPH

Name(s) ______________________

Date ______________________

Favorite Games and Stories

Animal Friends

PHOTOGRAPH

Name(s)

Date

PHOTOGRAPH

Name(s)

Date

Favorite Foods

A Favorite Outfit

PHOTOGRAPH

Name(s) ______________________

Date ______________________

Birthdays

Birthdays

Holidays and Celebrations

Holidays and Celebrations

Holidays and Celebrations

Holidays and Celebrations

Baby's Measurements

Doctor's name ______

Address ______

Phone ______

Infant and childhood illnesses	Date

	Height	Weight
at birth		
1 week		
2 weeks		
3 weeks		
1 month		
2 months		
3 months		
4 months		
5 months		
6 months		
9 months		
12 months		
18 months		
24 months		

Immunizations

Vaccine	Date of dose				
Diphtheria, Tetanus, and Pertussis					
Polio					
Measles, Mumps, and Rubella					
H. *Influenzae* Type B					
Hepatitis B					
Other					

Published simultaneously in Canada by HarperCollins*CanadaLtd*
Color separations by Prestige Graphics
Printed and bound in the United States by Berryville Graphics
First edition, 1996

The Carl character originally appeared in *Good Dog, Carl*
by Alexandra Day, published by Green Tiger Press

Handprints at One Year

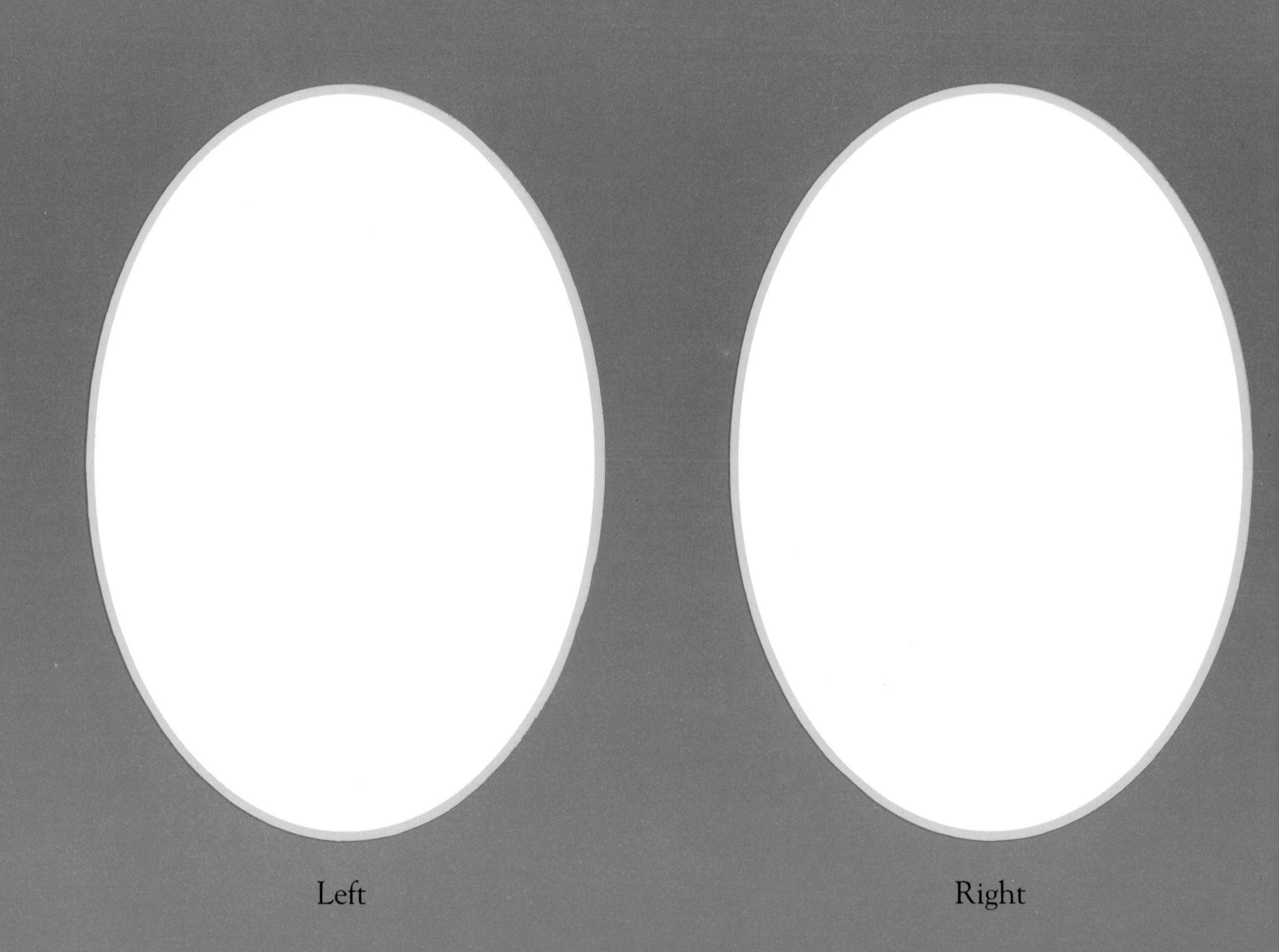